THE OUTCROP QUIZ

A picture book of puzzles for
geology students of all ages

JOHN WRIGHT

London
ALLEN & UNWIN
Boston   Sydney

Allen & Unwin (Publishers) Ltd,
40 Museum Street, London WC1A 1LU, UK

Allen & Unwin (Publishers) Ltd,
Park Lane, Hemel Hempstead, Herts HP2 4TE, UK

Allen & Unwin, Inc.,
8 Winchester Place, Winchester, Mass. 01890, USA

Allen & Unwin (Australia) Ltd,
8 Napier Street, North Sydney, NSW 2060, Australia

First published in 1986

British Library Cataloguing in Publication Data

Wright, John, 1931–
   The outcrop quiz: a picture book of puzzles for
geology students of all ages.
1.   Geology, Structural—Problems, exercises, etc.
I.   Title
551.8'076   QE601.8
ISBN 0–04–550041–X

Library of Congress Cataloging-in-Publication Data

Wright, John, 1931–
   The outcrop quiz.
Bibliography: p.
Includes index.
1.   Geology—Field work—Examinations, questions, etc.
2.   Geology, Structural—Examinations, questions, etc.
I.   Title.
QE45.W76   1986   551.8   86–1097
ISBN 0–04–550041–X (pbk.: alk. paper)

Printed in Great Britain by Butler & Tanner Ltd,
Frome and London

Acknowledgements

I'm grateful to several generations of Open University geology students for helping me to keep alive the idea of this book. Grateful thanks are also due to Colin Bagshaw, Angela Colling, Sheilah Dellow and Jack Thomas for working through various stages of the Quiz and making many helpful comments and suggestions. They are, of course, not to be held responsible for any errors or other shortcomings.

Introduction

Can you always tell the difference between anticlines and synclines, joints and faults, unconformities and disconformities, concretions and conglomerates, bedding and cleavage, strike and dip, apparent dip and true dip? If your answer to all that is a firm yes, then stop reading right now. If not ...

This book offers entertainment and challenge, satisfaction and enlightenment, to anyone who knows a bit of geology but hasn't had much chance to study rocks in outcrop. The entertainment and challenge come from looking at the pictures and trying the questions. The satisfaction comes from the answers you get right, the enlightenment from finding out where you went wrong.

As well as being fun, the book should help those budding geologists who find it difficult to relate the often messy reality of outcrops to the neat and tidy theory of textbook diagrams. The geologist needs to 'get his eye in', to see through the camouflage of vegetation, soil, scree, and so on, and to read the underlying story.

The pictures and questions in this book will give you practice in doing that. You'll also find plenty of opportunity to improve your understanding of those often elusive and baffling concepts, strike and dip, and to develop your skill in handling them.

The puzzles are intended to get progressively more difficult, but you could well find that some of the earlier problems are harder to solve than later ones — it depends very much on your own particular background. If you find you can't answer a particular question, then leave it and come back to it later.

Interpreting outcrops is more a matter of recognising relationships between rocks than of precisely identifying the rocks themselves. You can often tell whether you're dealing with sedimentary, igneous or metamorphic rocks, and that's usually all you need in order to recognise structures and sort out their orientation. Details in the rocks themselves may enable you to distinguish, say, a limestone from a sandstone or a granite from a basalt, but you'll be surprised how often you can decipher the essentials of a story without needing to know just what the rocks are.

An outcrop can be interesting without being spectacular. The superficially dull roadside cutting, for instance, generally repays a second look. Once you get your eye in, you find that beneath its bland exterior there lies a wealth of detail about structure, rock type, weathering patterns, and so on. Some of the pictures have been specially selected to make this very point.

The photographs are in black and white. Colour can be both a help and a hindrance when interpreting outcrops. Rocks of different colour stand out from one another, and colour can be a guide to identification. On the other hand, soil creep, weathering, screes, and so on, can produce misleading patterns of colour and obscure the relationships you want to interpret.

The pictures show outcrops on all scales, from the landscape to the close-up. There's geology to be seen almost anywhere you go — even in the building stones of towns and cities — and if you keep your eyes open as you travel about, you can devise your own Outcrop Quiz.

Enjoy yourself.

1. This outcrop is about 20 m high. What is this type of linear structure called, and how does it develop?

2. What is this kind of feature called, and how did this example form? (It is about 25 m high.)

3. What is the cause of this landscape pattern?

5. This outcrop is about 1.5 m across.
(a) Can you offer two explanations of the somewhat irregular white pattern in the lower half of the outcrop, which is the surface of a bed?
(b) Where are the ripple marks, and what do they tell you about current directions during deposition of the sediments?

4. This is an aerial view. The ground rises gently towards the skyline, which is the top of a broad ridge about 1 km away. What might the lines of holes represent? (The large one at lower left is 3−4 m across.)

6. (a) What pattern of bedding is particularly well developed in the middle and left of this outcrop?
(b) In what direction did the currents flow during deposition of this part of the sequence?

7. Concentrate on the pale layer in the middle of this outcrop, below the hammer.
(a) What are the undulations in this layer, how did they form, and what was the direction of sediment transport?
(b) When did the large block below the hammer fall into this layer?
(c) What is the origin of the large block?

8. (a) Of what rock type is this weathering pattern characteristic,
and what is the main cause of the pattern?
(b) What is the probable attitude of the bedding?
(c) Can you identify at least one major joint direction that might
have helped to control the weathering?

9. This outcrop is about 2 m across, and has been naturally sand-blasted. Which way was the wind blowing?

10. (a) What rock type forms the major part of this outcrop?
(b) In what direction is the dip, and what is the approximate dip
angle?
(c) What has caused the overhangs on the left?

11. This outcrop is 3−4 m across.
(a) What are the sub-spherical bodies called?

(b) How do they form?
(c) In what rock type have they formed here?

12. (a) How can you tell from this distance whether these rocks
are igneous (volcanic or plutonic), sedimentary or metamorphic?
(b) How does the outcrop pattern develop?
(c) Can you infer anything about the composition of the rocks?

13. (a) What are the rounded structures in this outcrop?
(b) Have the rocks been tilted since they were formed?
(c) Can you tell in which direction the rocks get younger?

14. (a) What causes the structure or pattern developed in the upper two-thirds of this outcrop (where the hammer is)?
(b) In what kinds of rocks is it best developed?
(c) Another kind of structure or pattern is somewhat crudely developed in the lower third of the outcrop. Can you identify it, and does that help you to make more-specific inferences about the rocks here?

15. (a) What is the near-vertical feature in the middle of this outcrop? (It is sheet-like in form, it extends from the bottom nearly to the top of the picture, and you are looking at it edge-on.)
(b) Is it younger or older than the surrounding rocks?
(c) What evidence suggests that the surrounding rocks are more likely to be of plutonic igneous origin than of volcanic igneous, sedimentary or metamorphic origin?
(d) What can you deduce about relative cooling rates, and hence about relative levels of emplacement?
(e) Could you determine a strike and dip here?

16. (a) Of what is this rock chiefly composed?
(b) What can you infer about its probable composition and age?
(c) Is this likely to be a fresh or a weathered outcrop surface?

17. This outcrop is about 50 cm across. The rock is a massive limestone. Does this structure result from natural causes?

18. You are looking at a hillside that slopes down towards you.
(a) Are the beds on the right horizontal?
(b) What is the most likely explanation for the absence of outcrop on the left? (The near-horizontal white line in the upper left is a sheep track.)

19. This vertical face is about 8 m high.
(a) What kind of mine or quarry is this?
(b) Which is the downthrow side of the faults, and what is the approximate relative displacement along them?
(c) What is the approximate *average* dip of the fault planes?
(d) Do the faults die out upwards or downwards?

20. (a) What is this kind of topography called?
(b) What does it tell you about the underlying geology?

21. (a) In which direction do the rocks dip in the lower left of this outcrop?
(b) In which direction do the rocks dip in the rest of the outcrop?

(c) Which set of rocks is probably older?
(d) What is the probable nature of the discontinuity between the two rocks?

22. (a) Do the beds dip in the same direction on both sides of this outcrop? Do they strike in the same direction?

(b) What is the probable trend (strike) of the near-vertical discontinuity in the middle of the outcrop, in relation to the strike of the beds?

(c) What kind of discontinuity is it?

23. These massive beds are limestone.
(a) What is the attitude of the strata? Why could you not measure
a strike direction here?
(b) Are there any prominent joints?
(c) What is the main mechanism by which the cliffs retreat?

Here, and at intervals later, you will find questions about directions of strike and dip with respect to points of the compass. For these questions you are told in which direction the camera is pointing. If you line up the compass rose in Figure 1 with that direction, it may help you to determine the direction of strike and dip more easily.

The best way to use Figure 1 is probably to make a quick tracing of it and to use that as an overlay on the relevant pictures.

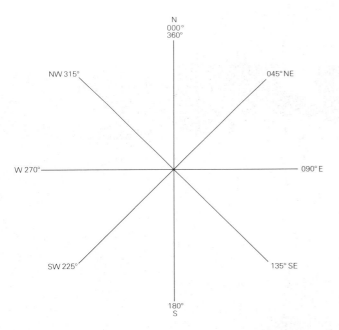

Figure 1   The compass rose, for use with items relating to direction of strike and dip.

24.   The camera is pointing north-east.
(a) In which direction do the beds get younger?
(b) Why would you get a reliable strike measurement by sighting along the waterline in the middle of the picture?
(c) What is the strike and approximate dip?

25. The camera is pointing WNW.
(a) In which direction would you go to look for the base of this sequence?
(b) How could you measure the strike and dip of these beds accurately without moving from the camera position?
(c) What is the strike and dip?

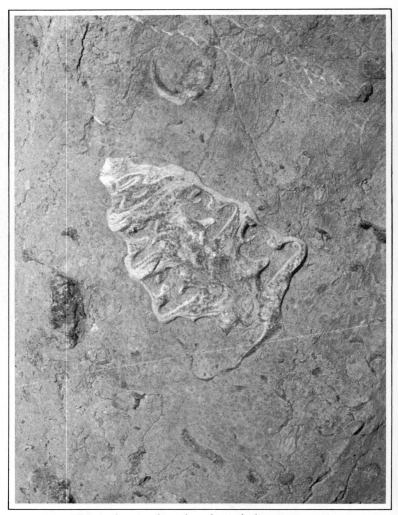

26. This is the weathered surface of a limestone outcrop. Of what organism is this a cross section? (It is about 10 cm long.)

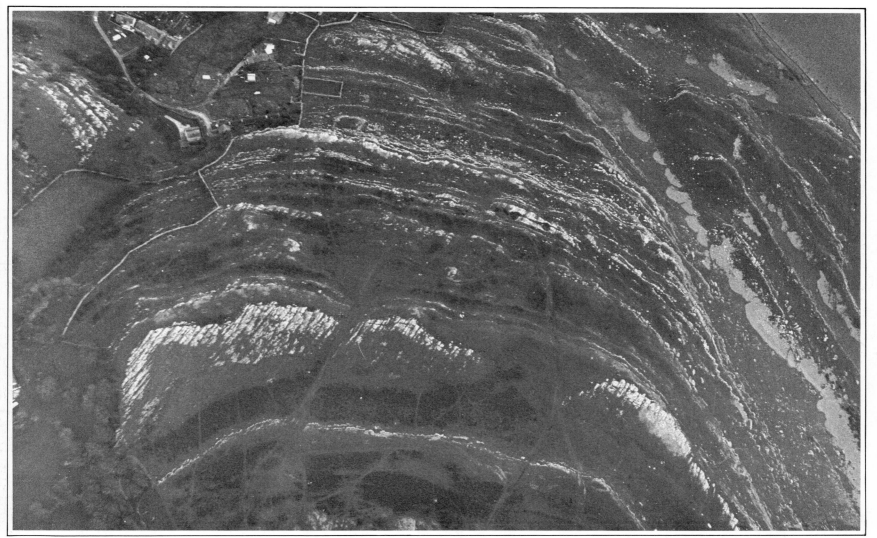

27. The camera is pointing almost vertically downwards. The coastline is visible in the upper right. North is at the bottom of the picture.
(a) Explain how you could tell that the bedding must be gently dipping or horizontal.

(b) What is the approximate trend and probable attitude of the joints visible in the outcropping beds?

28. Most of this outcrop is an approximately vertical face about 50 cm high. It is the side of a low wall-like feature formed by a basaltic dyke outcropping on a shore. The irregular joint pattern is due to very crude horizontal columnar jointing. The somewhat darker area at the bottom is country rock sloping steeply away from the vertical dyke margin, i.e. towards you. There are two possible explanations for the myriad small cavities on the surface of the outcrop. What are they, and which do you consider to be more probable?

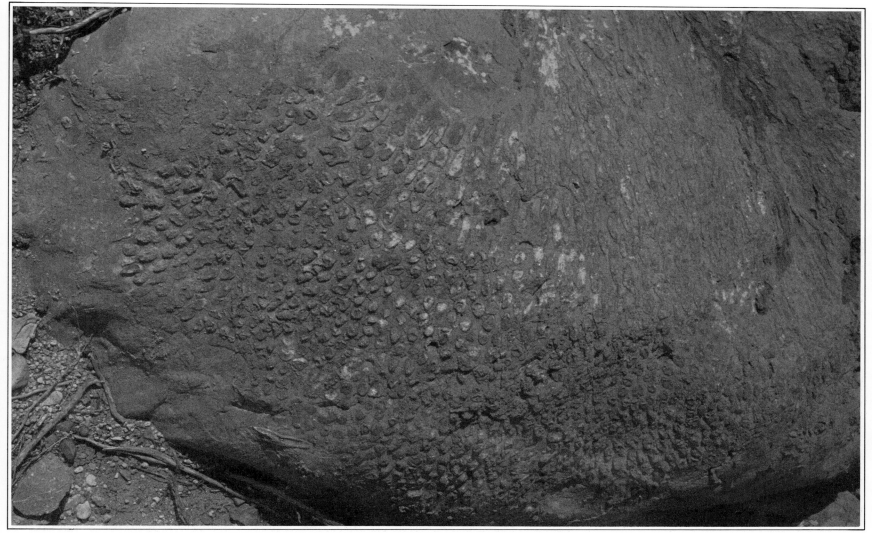

29. What organism makes up most of this outcrop, which is about 50 cm across?

30. This is a bedding surface in sandy siltstones, seen from above. The outcrop is about 50 cm across. What is the origin of the sub-circular and irregular darker patches?

31. This is a bedding surface in silty sandstones, seen from above. The outcrop is about 30 cm across. What organisms are seen here in cross section?

32. This outcrop is about 3 m across.
(a) Can you distinguish bedding from joints?
(b) What kind of tectonic explanation might account for the form of the white band in the middle of the outcrop?
(c) What non-tectonic explanation is also possible?
(d) Which of the two explanations do you think more probable?

33. This outcrop is 4–5 m high.
(a) What environment of deposition is suggested by the stratification and by the rock types?

(b) Is the dip of layering depositional or structural?
(c) To what do you attribute the discontinuities in the outcrop?

34. (a) In which direction do these beds dip?
(b) To what kind of discontinuity is the person pointing?
(c) Were the beds tilted before or after the discontinuity developed?
(d) What is the probable nature of the rocks to the left of the discontinuity?

35. (a) What kind of boundary is probably represented by the discontinuity between the darker rocks on the left and the lighter rocks on the right, given that it is not a fault?

(b) Which set of rocks is the younger?

(c) What can you say about the strike and dip of bedding?

(d) Does the outcrop suggest a tensional or compressional environment at the time of formation of the younger rocks?

(e) What can you say about the nature of the rocks on either side of the boundary?

36. This outcrop is about 8 m high.
(a) What evidence is there that the lens in the middle is part of the main sediment sequence?
(b) Are the dips mainly depositional, structural or due to compaction?
(c) What rocks might be represented here, and hence what is the probable origin of the lens?

37. These two pictures show different parts of the same outcrop. The upper one (a) is less than 50 cm across, the lower one (b) about 3 m across. You are looking at beds edge-on. What sedimentary structures suggest that the beds might be inverted?

39. The camera is pointing north-east.
What is the approximate strike and dip of these beds?

38. This outcrop is about 2 m across.
(a) Which has the steeper dip — cleavage or bedding?
(b) Which of the two is more obvious, and how can you distinguish them?
(c) What are the rocks, and what were they originally?

40. (a) Which of these two rock types is the younger, the darker or the lighter?

(b) Are the rocks likely to be igneous, sedimentary or metamorphic, and how could this assemblage have formed?

41. This outcrop is 2−3 m across.
(a) What is the approximate displacement on the fault, and which is the downthrow side?
(b) The outcrop shows evidence of one phase of plastic deformation and two of brittle deformation, all resulting from tensional stress.
Can you place them in sequence and explain why the fault comes third?
(c) What type of rocks might these be?

42. The camera is pointing WNW. The cliff is about 10 m high.

(a) What is the approximate strike and the approximate dip of the block in the centre foreground?

(b) Where is the igneous body, and what would you call it?

(c) Did the igneous activity occur before or after the sediments were tilted?

43. The camera is pointing east.
(a) How can you tell that this sequence consists of alternating more and less resistant layers?
(b) How can you tell that the camera is pointing directly along strike? What is the strike?
(c) How could you measure the dip accurately without moving from the camera position? What is the dip?

(d) Draw a sketch map of the outcrop of the layer forming the dip slope in the left foreground. Put one strike and dip symbol where the layer outcrops in the foreground, another about half way up the slope below the building. Use the symbol ⅄ , rather than the dip arrow ⇘ .

44. This outcrop is about 3 m high.
(a) What is the approximate total vertical displacement on the fault, and which is the downthrow side?
(b) With the help of a sketch, show why this is not a simple single-plane fault, as might appear at first sight.

(c) How can you tell that the faulting resulted from tension, not compression?

45. This outcrop is 3–4 m high.
(a) What would you call the basic structure?
(b) Where is the erosional discontinuity, and does it suggest a major break in deposition?

(c) Are beds above the erosional break thicker to the right or the left of the fault?
(d) What can you infer about the timing of faulting, erosion and deposition?

46. This is a plan view. You are looking at a sub-horizontal surface. North is at the top. The outcrop is about 50 cm across.
(a) Is this an isoclinal fold?
(b) What is the approximate orientation of the fold axial plane?
(c) What is the approximate trend and plunge of the fold axis?
(d) Can you tell whether the fold is an anticline or a syncline?

47. This outcrop is about 2 m high.
(a) What is the orientation of the fold axial plane?
(b) Do the beds thin and thicken along fold limbs and round hinges?
(c) This is a small parasitic fold on the limb of a much larger fold. Is it an S-fold or a Z-fold?
(d) Sketch a simple cross section to show the approximate form of the major fold to which this one is parasitic.

48. (a) Why can these be described both as neutral folds and as chevron folds?
(b) Identify more − and less − competent layers by the way in which they have been affected by the folding.

49. This is an oblique aerial view, looking north-east. The white is snow. The topmost part of the picture (white at left, dark at right) is the surface of a plateau.

(a) Can you explain the outcrop pattern, and make an estimate of strike and dip?

(b) Attempt a geological sketch map of the outcrop pattern, with strike and dip symbols. Sketch a NE−SW cross section for your map.

50. (a) What evidence suggests the presence of two rock types
here?
(b) What might the age relationships be?
(c) What can you infer about the rock types?

51. This outcrop is 2−3 m high. The rocks were affected by a diagenetic process and by a tectonic process. What are those processes, and which came first?

52. This outcrop is about 1 m high.
(a) What is the approximate displacement on the fault?
(b) Why does the angle of dip of the fault vary down the outcrop?
(c) Why is the fault occupied by a vein, and why does the thickness of the vein vary down the outcrop?
(d) What might the rock types be?

53. This outcrop is 8–10 m high. The flat-lying sediments are mainly limestones and calcareous shales. What can you infer about other rock types and about the sequence of geological events?

54. This outcrop is 8–10 m high. The darker sediments above are relatively coarse grits and sands, the paler beds below are silts and clays. There are similar relationships further along the cutting in both directions. (The dark vertical bands in the lower left and right are trees.) What could have happened to produce this structure?

55. Both of these blocks are 30–40 cm high. Compare and contrast the mode of origin of the two rocks.

56. What are these objects called, and how do they form? (They are about 10 cm across.)

57. How much can you infer about the rocks outcropping on this hillside?

The use of stone for the construction and decoration of buildings is as old as civilisation.

Rocks used for ornamental stone are chosen because they are handsome, and many are easy to recognise (even in black and white). Rocks used for ordinary building stone are normally selected for properties other than appearance, but many have distinctive textures or other features that enable you to identify them.

58. This is a monomineralic rock, used in the construction of a palace several thousands of years ago, the ruins of which have been open to the weather for many centuries. The rock is more often used for sculpture and statuary than as a building stone.

(a) What is the probable cause of the grooves in the white and finer-grained, more-massive block on the left?

(b) What is the crystallographic property displayed by the large crystal in the coarse-grained block shown above?

(c) What is the common term for the rock, and what mineral forms it?

59. This column and its base are part of a Greco-Roman temple. (a) Are both made of the same stone?

(b) With the help of the close-up view on the right, what can you infer about the rock used to make the column?

60. (a) What stone was used in the construction of this Victorian building?
(b) Is the bedding inverted in any of the blocks?

Answers

1. Columnar jointing. It develops as a result of contraction during the cooling and solidification of igneous sheets. The columns are ideally hexagonal in cross section, but are often simply polygonal. They typically (ideally) form perpendicular to cooling surfaces. They are best seen in lavas, sills and dykes of basaltic composition — as here — but are not uncommon in other igneous rocks. They sometimes develop in well-baked, fine-grained, sedimentary rocks at igneous contacts.

2. Sea stacks. The rocks here dip gently towards the right and towards the camera. They are well bedded, with strong joints approximately parallel to and at right angles to the coastline. These are ideal conditions for the formation of sea stacks, the other principal requirement being relatively deep water up to the base of the cliffs. Weathering exploits joints and bedding planes, and the cliffs retreat as loosened joint blocks are prised out by the impact of large waves. Blocks that are larger or more resistant, or both, are left standing as stacks.
(Limestones.)

3. Abandoned meanders on a river floodplain have left a complex pattern of oxbow lakes. Successive stages of present meanders can also be seen, as series of approximately concentric sand bars deposited on the 'inside' curves of the river.

4. At first sight they look like sinkholes in limestone country, but they go up the slope in straight lines that form both *en echelon* and mutually perpendicular patterns. The margins of the holes are raised, forming circular *'levees'*. They are more likely to be excavations made along mineralised veins which follow major joints. This is, in fact, limestone country, so an initial identification of sinkholes is quite plausible.

5. (a) The white pattern is either due to fossil mud cracks formed on the dessicated bed of an ancient lagoon, lake or pool, then filled by sandy or silty sediments blown or washed in soon afterwards; or due to shrinkage cracks formed by chemical changes during lithification and then filled by minerals (e.g. calcite) deposited from solutions that later moved through the rocks. There is not enough evidence here to be sure of either explanation, but the thin beds and the ripple marks (see (b)) tend to favour the first one.
(b) Fossil ripple marks are visible on at least one bedding plane in the upper half of the outcrop. Their alignment is more or less towards the camera, so current (or wave) motions were approximately at right angles to this direction.

6. (a) Cross-bedding or current-bedding. It is well developed here, with topset, foreset and bottomset components identifiable.
(b) Here the currents flowed from right to left.
(Water-laid volcanic ashes.)

7. (a) The undulations are ripples, formed either by water or by wind. They are asymmetrical, and show that the direction of transport was from right to left.
(b) Disturbance of layering near the block suggests that it fell into the rippled layer when about two-thirds of the layer's thickness had accumulated. More fine sediment was then deposited on top. Subsequent compaction caused overlying beds to be very gently arched over the block.
(c) If the sediments were waterlain, one possible explanation is that the block is a 'dropstone', released from melting ice (or from the roots of a tree that floated out to sea or into a lake and then decayed), then falling into soft sediment.
  If the sediments were sub-aerial, the block either fell from a nearby cliff, or it was a projectile, such as a volcanic bomb. In fact, this is the case here.

8. (a) The weathering pattern is characteristic of relatively pure and massively bedded limestones. Solution by acid rain waters and ground waters enlarges joints and joint intersections to form solution channels. The potholes in the foreground could also have been enlarged by pebbles swirling round in vortices and abrading the walls. The setting of this outcrop suggests that such vortices might have been associated with vigorous wave action rather than strong river flow, which would imply that sea level was once higher than it is now. Other evidence would be needed to confirm or refute such inferences.
(b) The bedding is virtually horizontal, picked out by differential weathering of small lithological contrasts in the layering, to give the appearance of rough contour lines round the walls of the potholes.
(c) A major joint intersection trends from lower right to upper left, defined by the line of potholes in the foreground. There is probably another set of joints at right angles to this.

9. The wind blew mainly from left to right. Leeward surfaces, facing to the right, are steeper and rougher than windward surfaces, which are gently undulating, smoothed and grooved.

10. (a) Conglomerate, made up of rounded boulders and pebbles in a finer-grained matrix.
(b) The dip is to the right at about 20–25°.
(c) The overhangs on the left are due to differential erosion of more and less resistant layers, possibly finer- and coarser-grained or well and poorly

cemented. The major overhang at the bottom of the visible sequence results from weathering out of a finer-grained layer.

11. (a) They are concretions, almost spherical enough to be called cannonball concretions.
(b) They form during lithification or diagenesis, or both, as migrating pore waters precipitate cements (usually calcareous) round suitable nucleation centres, or perhaps along coarser layers in the sediments − as suggested by the pebbles in the concretions in the lower right.
(c) The rock is a siltstone or fine sandstone, with thin pebble bands and lenses.

12. (a) These are probably either plutonic igneous rocks or very high grade homogeneous metamorphic rocks (granulitic or granitic gneisses), which are formed under comparable conditions of temperature and pressure.
   The absence of visible bedding or layering rules out sedimentary or volcanic igneous rocks. The lack of obvious foliation (schistosity) or banding eliminates most metamorphic rocks.
(b) The outcrop pattern results from exfoliation of large joint blocks in the massive homogeneous rocks. It may be a purely mechanical process (differential expansion and contraction caused by diurnal heating and cooling, perhaps aided by expansion as erosion removes overlying rock); but it is more likely to be a combination of physical and chemical processes − spheroidal weathering on a large scale, in short. Joint blocks become rounded because corners and edges are more susceptible to attack than plane surfaces.
(c) Only limited inferences are possible regarding composition. The rocks seem to be fairly pale in colour, and the outcrop is sparsely vegetated. In general, acid to intermediate plutonic rocks (granite, diorite and syenite, in order of relative abundance) are of lighter colour and are less rapidly weathered than basic rocks (gabbros). As a group, they are also more common in the continental crust.
   Identification as granite or diorite stands a fair chance of being correct (and is, in this case). However, not all gabbros are dark, and under the right climatic conditions they can form resistant outcrops of exfoliated blocks. In addition, massive, regionally metamorphosed, impure quartzites or marbles could also form large outcrops like this one.

13. (a) The upper central part of the outcrop shows good cross sections through lava pillows, formed by the eruption of (usually basaltic) lava under water. You should be able to discern that the margins are slightly different from the interiors − the result of different grain size − and there are faint signs of radial fracturing in the marginal zones.
(b) Lava pillows tend to be slightly flattened, and therefore ovoid rather than circular in cross section. The vertical elongation of the best-developed pillows, in the upper centre of the outcrop, coupled with some signs of steep stratification − on the right, for instance − suggests that the rocks have been tilted to within about 20° of the vertical since they were formed.
(c) Overlying pillows tend to be concave towards underlying ones. Virtually the only example here is in the upper centre, but it is enough to indicate that the lavas are probably younger towards the right.

14. (a) The pattern is due to spheroidal weathering, the result of preferential attack by rain water and ground water along edges and corners of joint blocks. Hydration of more-easily weathered feldspars and ferromagnesian minerals causes expansion, and the weathered rock peels away in layers, eventually leading to the formation of near-spherical 'corestones'.
(b) It is usually best seen in igneous rocks, because these tend to be homogeneous and joints are the main discontinuities in them. Basic rocks are generally more susceptible than acid rocks, because they have a higher proportion of relatively easily weathered minerals.
(c) The lower third of the outcrop shows crude columnar jointing, and the surfaces are pitted as though they might be vesicular. The implication is that the outcrop could be of a weathered lava flow (or sill). If you inferred that the rock is basaltic, you would be correct, though an intermediate composition is also possible.

15. (a) An igneous dyke. It is straight and regular, and it could be of basaltic composition, though you cannot be certain of that from the picture alone.
(b) It cuts the surrounding rocks, and is therefore younger.
(c) The rocks are coarse-grained. There is no visible layering, banding or preferred orientation of minerals.
(d) The coarse-grained country rocks cooled slowly. They were emplaced at a depth of several kilometres. The fine-grained dyke cooled quickly. It was emplaced at a shallow depth after erosion had partly or completely unroofed the plutonic rocks. Subsequent erosion has lowered the land surface still further, exposing both rocks.
(e) The strike of the dyke is virtually in line with the camera, and its dip is about 80° to the right.
(Basalt and monzonite.)

16. (a) The rock is composed almost entirely of crinoid fragments (ossicles), seen both in transverse (circular) and longitudinal sections. There are smaller fragments of broken crinoid skeletons between the larger ones.
(b) The rock is limestone. The presence of crinoid remains suggests an age of either Upper Palaeozoic or Mesozoic. If this outcrop is in Britain, the rock is probably Carboniferous in age.
(c) It is a weathered surface. Only differential 'etching' by weathering solutions could make fossil fragments stand out so well from the enclosing matrix.

17. This type of fracture pattern is produced by blasting. The centre of the radial pattern is probably the base of the original shot hole drilled for the explosive. These structures are common in quarries and other excavations (e.g. cuttings) in hard rock.
(Massive limestone.)

18. (a) The outcropping layers on the right appear to be nearly horizontal, but some of the small overhangs suggest gentle dips away from you, especially in the upper right. Some overhangs look horizontal, but this is probably because of downhill sagging of unsupported joint blocks, due to soil creep.

(b) A fault has probably brought less-resistant beds to lie against these exposed layers. It is probably a normal fault, as the layers have not been tilted much from their original horizontal position. The line of the fault, and signs of fault drag in exposed layers (down to the left), suggest that the downthrow is to the left.

19. (a) An open-pit coal mine. The upper coal seam is less than 50 cm thick, the lower one is more than 1 m thick.
(b) The downthrow side is to the left, and the relative displacement is about 50 cm at the level of the upper seam, for both faults.
(c) The *average* dip is to the left, and at about 70° on the right-hand fault, about 60° on the left-hand fault (measured with a protractor from top to bottom of the face, on the photograph). There is some variation, especially in the upper seam, where the dips of the fault planes are less, perhaps due to refraction.
(d) The faults can easily be seen above the upper seam, where they displace two thin, darker grey beds near the top of the face. They are less easy to see below the upper seam, but there are two thin, pale grey layers in which displacements can be seen. At the bottom of the face, both faults have virtually died out into small monoclinal folds.

20. (a) Scarp and dip slope topography (also known as scarp and vale topography).
(b) The underlying geology consists of alternating layers of more and less resistant layers dipping gently to the right (at about 5° here). The edges of 'harder' layers form the scarp slopes and the dip slopes develop where 'softer' layers have been eroded away. Alternations of shales with limestones or sandstones are the commonest cause of this kind of topography.

21. (a) The rocks in the lower left dip steeply (about 45°) to the left.
(b) The rocks in the rest of the outcrop dip moderately (about 30°) away from you and slightly to the right.
(c) The rocks in the lower left are probably older (but see (d)).
(d) The discontinuity is probably an unconformity which dips in the same direction as the rocks in the upper part of the outcrop. However, it *could* be a thrust fault, in which case the rocks in the lower left *could* be younger.
(Sandstones and limestones unconformable on phyllites.)

22. (a) The beds dip towards the right on both sides of the outcrop, at about 30° on the left and about 60° on the right. The strike direction is approximately in line with the camera on both sides of the outcrop.
(b) The discontinuity is a plane, and its strike probably coincides with that of the beds.
(c) The discontinuity is a fault, probably downthrowing to the right, judging from the signs of drag on the right-hand side of the outcrop. It could not be a tilted unconformity, as neither set of beds is parallel to it, nor is there evidence of a basal conglomerate (though this is not, of itself, conclusive).

23. (a) The beds are almost horizontal. By definition, strike is a horizontal line, and you can draw an infinite number of horizontal lines on a horizontal surface, in any direction. A horizontal surface can have no strike direction.
(b) One set of prominent joints is approximately parallel to the plane of the picture. There seems to be another set, less well developed, at approximately right angles to the main set, also vertical, and trending towards the camera.
(c) Two layers of massive limestone are separated by more-thinly bedded and less-resistant sediments, e.g. clays, marls and sandy limestones (the lower parts of this thinly bedded sequence are obscured by fallen blocks on the prominent 'shelf' about halfway down the cliff). These less-resistant beds are preferentially eroded, leaving large, unsupported blocks of massive limestone, which are loosened by water penetrating along the joints, and which eventually fall.

24. (a) The beds dip to the right (the south-east) and must get younger in that direction (assuming they have not been overturned).
(b) The strike is by definition the orientation of a horizontal line on an inclined plane. Still water surfaces are horizontal. The intersection of a still water surface with an inclined plane will define the strike.
(c) The camera is 'looking' along the waterline, and hence along the strike, which must be NE−SW. The waterline is not quite straight because bedding planes always have some irregularities or undulations, however slight. The most reliable strike reading would be obtained by sighting along the 'best-fit' straight line through the gentle curves of the waterline. As the camera is pointing north-east, the strike bearing is close to 050−230°. The dip is 10−15° towards the south-east.
(Sandstones.)

25. (a) The beds dip to the left (southerly), so the base of the sequence must lie to the right (towards the north), assuming the beds have not been overturned.
(b) The camera is 'looking' edge-on along the topmost bed of the main outcrop (aberrant dips in the right foreground are on fallen blocks). The strike could be measured very accurately by taking a bearing from the camera position to the intersection between the topmost bedding plane and the horizon. The dip could be measured very accurately by holding the clinometer at arm's length and lining up the edge with the topmost bedding plane, using the horizon as the horizontal reference line.
(c) The strike is WNW−ESE, close to 290−110°. The dip is almost exactly 60° southerly.
(Thin-bedded impure limestones.)

26. It is a cross section through a gastropod shell. The spiral coiling pattern is clearly seen, and portions of the central columella are visible. The shell stands out because it is slightly more resistant to weathering than the host limestone.

27. (a) The outcrops of the beds approximate to contours. You can follow them along the steep slope down to the sea on the right, round the spur occupying most of the picture, and up the valley on the left. An approximate outcrop V-pattern can be seen in the upper left, its apex obscured by alluvial deposits in the valley. Where outcrops of strata resemble topographic contours, the beds must be nearly horizontal.

(b) The joints are best-developed in a prominent bed in the lower half of the picture. They trend approximately SSW—NNE, and they are probably steeply dipping or vertical.

28. The cavities could be vesicles, due to escape of gas from the cooling magma, or they could result from carious (honeycomb) weathering. The second explanation is more probable. Vesicles tend to be more abundant near the central portions of dykes than along margins. The cavities are so abundant over parts of the outcrop surface that the rock would be scoriaceous if they were vesicles — and scoria dykes are rare. Many of the cavities are a few centimetres across, larger than most vesicles.

This pattern results from a form of differential weathering, and it occurs in a great variety of rocks, on scales ranging from less than a centimetre to about 10 cm or more. The mechanism is not fully understood, and it remains a puzzle why uniform rocks such as basalts should have sufficient inhomogeneities to enable differential weathering to take place. Part of the explanation here might be that the rocks have been somewhat altered by hydrothermal fluids, and salt 'corrosion' by sea water has something to do with it, because carious weathering is most commonly (though *not* exclusively) seen on coasts.

29. It is a colonial coral. In the lower middle and on the left, you can see individual coral branches in sub-circular cross sections. On the right and higher up, you can see longitudinal sections.

30. They are the filled-in burrows of marine worms, which moved through the sediment vertically (sub-circular cross sections) or horizontally (irregular sections).

31. They are probably cross sections of bivalves. The five on the right are of single valves lying concave upwards. The one on the left is a cross section through both valves, and the animal might be preserved here in original life position. The substrate and the absence of internal skeletal remains, combined with the appearance of the cross sections, support identification of these as bivalves rather than as brachiopods.

32. (a) Bedding planes dip at about 20° to the left. Two good joints are visible in the left half of the outcrop, almost exactly perpendicular to the bedding, dipping at 70° to the right. The camera is pointing along the strike of both bedding and joints.
(b) The pinch-and-swell aspect of the white layer suggests boudinage structure, the result of tectonic stretching.
(c) The material in the white layer was either originally deposited in this lensoid form, or it represents material redissolved and reprecipitated in approximately nodular form during lithification and diagenesis.
(d) The second explanation seems more likely, because the bedding is regular and there is no evidence of deformation elsewhere in the outcrop. (Limestone with chert bands.)

33. (a) The stratification suggests that the sediments, which are gravels and sands, occupy overlapping channels in a former vigorous, and possibly braided, river system that flowed approximately at right angles to the outcrop face.
(b) The dips are depositional, not structural — a situation typical in this sort of sedimentary environment.
(c) The discontinuities result from the cross-cutting relationships between the different channels.

In more detail, the oldest channel forms the main triangular part of the outcrop. Changes of lithology within it suggest fluctuations in current speed. Two younger channels flank the main one to left and right. They also experienced fluctuations in flow. The role of the overhanging block in the upper left cannot be determined from this viewpoint.

34. (a) The beds dip to the right.
(b) The discontinuity is a minor angular unconformity. It truncates bedding to the left. Bedding to the right is parallel with it.
(c) Both. Before the erosion which gave rise to the unconformity, the beds were tilted to the right by not much more than 10° (the unconformity truncates cross-bedding, which has a 'built-in' depositional dip). After the overlying sediments were deposited, the whole sequence was again tilted to the right, this time by about 40°.
(d) The rocks to the left of the unconformity, i.e. below it, are cross-bedded and most likely to be sandstones (above it they are mainly limestones and shales).

35. (a) The boundary is probably an igneous contact, because of the massive unlayered and unbanded, and somewhat irregularly jointed, aspect of the darker rocks. Faulting could have occurred along the boundary later, though there is no sign of fault drag on the layering. There is some evidence of contact metamorphism in the slightly darker zone of layered rocks along the contact.
(b) The darker set of rocks on the left is the younger, because they cut across the layering in the paler rocks on the right.
(c) The dip of bedding is virtually horizontal, and it is therefore meaningless to attempt a strike determination.
(d) The darker rocks on the left are an igneous intrusion, emplaced into the paler sediments on the right. Right up to the contact there is no disturbance of layering. This could only happen in a tensional environment, with fractures and faults, up which magma could rise to be permissively emplaced.
(e) The dark colour and massive aspect of the igneous rocks suggests a basaltic or doleritic composition, which is what they are. The sediments comprise alternations of more and less resistant beds, and are shales with impure sandstones and limestones.

36. (a) There is some thinning of beds immediately above the lens, especially on the right. The lens appears to pass laterally into rocks of similar aspect, but which are more-regularly layered, again especially on the right.
(b) The bedding diverges both above and below the lens, and this is most likely to be the result of compaction. Where the lens passes laterally into more regularly layered rocks, the dips are probably at least partly depositional.
(c) The rocks could be mainly limestones with thin interbedded shales,

and the lens would then be a reef of some kind (not necessarily a coral reef). An alternative explanation is that the rocks are sandstones and the lens represents a channel — but this is less likely, since the top would not be so convex in such a case. In fact, the lens is a limestone reef structure.

37. (Upper) The grain size in the middle layer becomes coarser upwards. Such reverse grading is not common in subaqueous sediments, though it is quite common in aeolian ones. These sediments are too coarse to be aeolian.
(Lower) The convex-upward structures could be cross sections of wave-like bed forms. They are more likely to be an inverted system of overlapping or migrating channels, the upper parts of which were planed flat by erosion.
(Sandstones.)

38. (a) Cleavage has the steeper dip, at about 80° to the left. Bedding also dips to the left, at about 20—25°.
(b) Cleavage is the more obvious. The rocks split (cleave) along it, but show no lithological change across cleavage planes. Bedding shows up as fainter lines that define minor lithological changes. In places the cleavage planes bend or kink slightly, or even break continuity, where they cross bedding.
(c) The rocks are slates, because the cleavage is regular and closely spaced and the rocks are fine-grained. They were originally muddy sediments, rich in clay minerals, which recrystallised to form the myriad minute mica crystals responsible for the cleavage.

39. The strike is almost exactly at right angles to the road, i.e. NW—SE (315—135°). The dip is to the north-east at about 30—40°. There is no component of dip from the cuttings towards the road, i.e. this is not a syncline. Bedding planes visible on the undersides of layers protruding from the cuttings all show the same uniform strike and dip.
(Silts and sands.)

40. (a) Discrete angular to rounded blocks and fragments of the darker rock are enclosed and enveloped within the lighter rock. The obvious conclusion is that the darker rocks are older — but see (b).
(b) The rocks do not have a metamorphic aspect, and there is no banding or preferred orientation of minerals. The outcrop could be a very coarse sedimentary breccia or conglomerate, but only two rock types can be distinguished and there is an enormous range in the size and shape of fragments. The most reasonable suggestions are that this is either a volcanic agglomerate or (more likely) an intrusion breccia formed when an acid to intermediate magma (granite, diorite or syenite) invaded a basic rock (gabbro) and stoped off and engulfed blocks of it.
A more sophisticated explanation is suggested by the rounded shape of several of the darker blocks. Both magmas could have been molten at the same time. The hotter basic magma invaded the cooler acid-to-intermediate magma and was chilled by it to form pillows similar to those that form underwater — hence the larger, rounded, dark blocks. The acid-to-intermediate magma remained liquid to a lower temperature than the basic magma, and was mobile enough to form veins cutting the (now solid) dark rock and to break pieces off — hence the smaller, angular, dark fragments.

41. (a) The displacement on the fault is approximately 10—20 cm, and the downthrow is to the left.
(b) The plastic deformation was first. It involved stretching or boudinage of the two thicker, paler and more-competent layers in the lower half of the outcrop, and the corresponding movement of darker, laminated, less-competent material, which 'flowed' from the bulges into the hollows.
The first phase of brittle deformation resulted in fracture of both competent and incompetent rocks, forming the pale cross-cutting veins. The second phase of brittle deformation was the fault, which probably formed much later. It cuts impartially and uniformly through all of the rocks, and it is not associated with any veining.
(c) The rocks have a sedimentary aspect, but the deformation suggests at least low-grade metamorphism. They are weakly foliated slaty rocks, with cleavage virtually parallel to bedding, and the pale layers and veins are quartzite and vein quartz respectively.

42. (a) The strike is approximately east—west (090—270°); the dip is about 70° to the south. The face of the cliff behind is mainly a dip slope of beds with similar strike and dip. Dip surfaces can be seen above and to the right of the central block, and out towards the point.
(b) The igneous body is a parallel-sided sheet, 1—2 m thick, cutting through the sediments near the cliff-top on the right, and dipping gently westwards. You could call it a sill, because it is more horizontal than vertical. You could call it a dyke, because it cuts the bedding at a high angle. It would be simplest to call it a minor sheet intrusion.
(c) The igneous sheet shows little sign of tectonic disturbance, so it was probably emplaced after the beds were tilted.
(Impure limestones and trachyte.)

43. (a) The outcrop 'ribs' in the foreground are separated by soil or sand, where less-resistant beds have been removed by erosion.
(b) The foreground is virtually horizontal, and the camera points straight along one of the outcrop 'ribs'. It also points exactly edge-on to the layer which forms the dip slope in the left foreground, where that layer outcrops on the slope (below the large bush). So the strike must be east—west (090—270°).
(c) The dip would be measured by holding the compass clinometer at arm's length and aligning the edge with the prominent layer just below the large bush (the same layer that forms the dip slope in the left foreground). Using a protractor on the photograph, the dip is close to 25°, towards the north.
(d) The sketch should resemble Figure A1.
(Impure limestones and shales.)

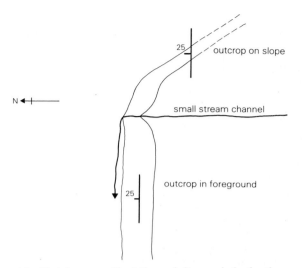

Figure A1 Sketch map with strike and dip symbols, for the answer to **43**. *Important:* north is shown at the left ONLY in order to match the orientation of the photograph.

44. (a) Using the base of the thick darker grey layer (gravels) as an obvious marker, the overall displacement is about 2 m vertically, with the downthrow to the left.
(b) The main fault bifurcates about halfway up the outcrop, so that the total displacement is the sum of two smaller throws (Fig. A2).
(c) These are normal faults. In such faults the downthrow side is *always* 'down the dip' of the fault plane. Normal faults result from tensional stresses. (All of the faults seen in preceding pictures are normal faults.)
(Fluviatile sands and gravels.)

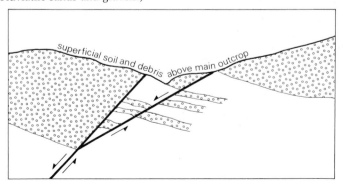

Figure A2 Sketch to show the fault pattern in **44**.

45. (a) The basic structure is that of a faulted monocline, both fault and fold dying out at the level of the upper pale layer.
(b) The erosional break is halfway up the sequence to the left of the fault (see Fig. A3). It does not represent a major break, since on the extreme left it is a disconformity only (there is no angular discordance). There can have been no tilting between the two episodes of deposition. The discordance of bedding near the fault must be due to erosion.
(c) The beds to the right of the fault are thicker than those to the left above the erosional break (which is not seen to the right of the fault).
(d) Sediments below the erosional break are not seen on the right, the downthrow side of the fault. Both faulting and erosion post-date deposition of these sediments. The fault continued to be active after deposition resumed, because sediments to the right of it are thicker than those to the left, up to and including the prominent pale layer. The fault was no longer active after deposition of this layer.
(Volcanic ash and fine scoria.)

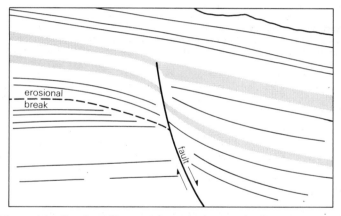

Figure A3 Sketch to illustrate the main features in **45**.

46. (a) Yes. The limbs are just about as parallel as they could be.
(b) The axial plane is near-vertical. At the southern end it trends almost exactly north–south, but then appears to swing slightly towards the north–east, due either to asymmetry of the fold or to an uneven surface on the exposure.
(c) The trend of the fold axis is close to north–south. The plunge is less easy to see and estimate. Bedding surfaces are quite well seen in the centre and towards the upper left. When these are followed round, it becomes apparent that the plunge is southward at perhaps 40–60° from the horizontal – it is not possible to be more precise than that.
(d) No. There is no way of telling whether the youngest layers are on the inside or the outside of the fold. However, if it were an anticline it would be overturned.
(Slates.)

47. (a) The strike of the fold axial plane is approximately in line with the camera, and the dip is about 20–25° to the right.
(b) Yes. The thin layers are generally more-widely separated at hinges than along limbs, suggesting some flowage of material during folding.
(c) You are looking along the axis of a fold which is nearly horizontal. This is an S-fold.
(d) We have no way-up information for the beds. This parasitic fold could lie either on the upper limb of a larger recumbent fold closing to the left, or on the lower limb of such a fold closing to the right (Fig. A4).
(Limestone and thin chert bands.)

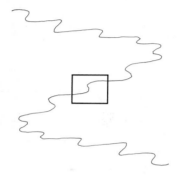

Figure A4 Sketch cross section to show the possible relationship of the fold in **47** to the larger recumbent fold.

48. (a) They are neutral folds, because axial planes are nearly horizontal, so without much-closer examination it is impossible to tell which beds are right way up and which overturned, and hence to distinguish anticlines from synclines.
(b) More competent layers (paler, standing slightly proud) have been deformed into folds of mainly parallel type: thickness perpendicular to bedding remains essentially constant on limbs and round hinges. However, in places, there is some thinning of limbs dipping to the left. Fractures nearly perpendicular to bedding in several of these layers are the result of tension during folding. Some of the less competent layers (darker, slightly recessed), especially the thicker ones, have been thinned along limbs and thickened at the hinges — the result of differential flow of softer (shaly) material during folding.
(Sandstones, siltstones, shales.)

49. (a) The outcrops are on the face (scarp slope) of an escarpment, cut in flat-lying or gently dipping beds. The edges of more-resistant beds form outcrop 'ribs' that are virtually parallel to topographic contours. The flat or gently sloping ground (dip slope) on top of the escarpment is formed by the upper surface of one of the beds.

The broad, inverted V-pattern of the outcrops is caused by the steep stream channel flowing down the scarp slope.
(b) Your sketches should resemble those in Figure A5.

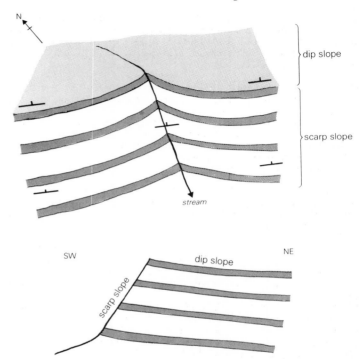

Figure A5 Sketch map and cross section to illustrate the relationships depicted in **49**. *Important:* beds are shown dipping gently north-east, but they could equally well be horizontal from the evidence on the photograph. The sketch map is orientated so as to be comparable with the photograph.

50. (a) Much of the middle and background is obscured by beach boulders, but there is enough outcrop in the left foreground to reveal approximately flat-lying sedimentary rocks. They are fairly thinly bedded and quite well jointed. The main joints are approximately at right angles and parallel to the main trend of the shoreline. The rocks have been weathered and eroded along the joints, so that bedding surfaces now look rather like pavements of large cobblestones. In the right foreground a 'causeway' heads out to sea, distinguished by closely spaced joints trending parallel to the main shoreline. Joints at right angles to this bisect and border the 'causeway', and are also well seen in the sedimentary rocks on its right.

(b) Clues to age relationships lie to the right of the 'causeway', where it cuts sedimentary layering. The boundary appears to be vertical, and one of the joint sets is parallel to it. The 'causeway' is younger than the sedimentary rocks.
(c) The 'causeway' is probably an igneous dyke. The straight parallel sides and good jointing are consistent with basaltic composition, but are not proof of it. Bedding in the sedimentary rocks rules out shales, but the available evidence does not permit more-positive identification.
(Basaltic dyke in sandstones.)

51. The irregular flat-to-ovoid bodies with a pinch-and-swell aspect just to the left of centre are concretions formed during diagenesis in the compacting and lithifying sediments.

A fault cuts the outcrop about halfway along, downthrowing to the left by about 1 m — the reference horizon is the thick concretionary layer partly obscured by vegetation in the upper right.

The fault post-dates the diagenesis.
(Marls with calcareous concretions.)

52. (a) The displacement is about 10 cm, and the downthrow is to the left. The reference layer is the approximately 10 cm thick bed that stands out slightly from the face just less than halfway down the outcrop to left of the fault, and about one-quarter of the way down the outcrop to the right of the fault.
(b) The dip angle of the fault varies because of refraction as it cuts through more and less competent beds. Faults are refracted away from the normal to the bedding plane where they pass from competent to incompetent layers. At the bottom of the outcrop the angle of dip has decreased to about 45°.
(c) The vein occupies the fault because of the refraction, and the variation in thickness is due to the same cause (see Fig. A6). The least-competent bed is at the bottom, and the very shallow angle of the fault there has prevented space becoming available for vein-filling material.
(d) The rock types are somewhat nodular shales and impure limestones, and the vein is of calcite. The competent layers could, however, be identified as sandstones, and the vein material as quartz.

53. The sediments are obviously cut by the dark, curved, sub-vertical sheet that occupies the upper central part of the outcrop and seems to be folded back on itself. It is obviously younger, and is likely to be an igneous rock — possibly basalt or dolerite. The sediments appear to be slightly more resistant to erosion adjacent to the sheet, especially on the left, which is consistent with baking and induration by contact metamorphism.

Sedimentary layering to the left of the sheet has been thrown down a few tens of centimetres relative to that on the right. A small fault extends below the sheet, on the right, and dies out at the base of the cliff.

This is a very unusual type of dyke intrusion. It appears to cut down through the sediments instead of up. The magma could have been travelling along a fracture, after reaching a high level in the crust (this must be a process that occurs where very long dykes are formed). If it then

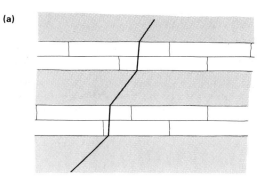

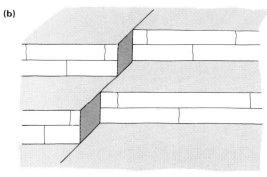

Figure A6 Diagrammatic sketches to illustrate the answer to **52.**
(a) Before faulting, to show the pattern of refraction, between more-competent (brick ornament) and less-competent (line ornament) beds.
(b) After faulting, to show how variable dip forms spaces that are filled by mineralising solutions.

encountered a solution cave or hollow in these predominantly calcareous rocks, it would have flowed down into the cavity. If the magma had cooled somewhat by this time, it could have been viscous and coherent enough to retain the sheet-like form, and this would account for the 'fold'.

54. This could be a compaction effect that occurred when the sediments were water-saturated. A sudden shock, such as a nearby fault movement triggering an earthquake, could have fluidised the sediments — as happens when a thixotropic gel is agitated. The load of sands and grits (plus other sediments which formerly overlay them) could then have collapsed into the much weaker silts and clays, expelling water and locally displacing them upwards, so that they appear to intrude the overlying beds. The process is similar to that which forms sand- or mud-volcanoes.

55. Both blocks consist of larger fragments or crystals in a finer-grained matrix.

In the left-hand block, the fragments range in size from 10 cm or more down to less than 1 cm. The variation in shades of grey suggests that different rock types may be present among the fragments. The fragments are all fine-grained. Their shape is highly irregular and variable. The rock is a breccia. It is of volcanic origin, i.e. an agglomerate. In the right-hand block, the white patches are crystals of approximately uniform size, mostly in the range 1–3 cm. They are (feldspar) phenocrysts in an igneous rock. They formed as the magma paused on its way to the surface and a period of slow cooling enabled large crystals to grow. The fine-grained matrix formed when the magma reached shallow crustal levels (probably not the surface in this case – the rock is rather coarse) and cooled more rapidly. It is also likely that the magma was richer in volatiles when the phenocrysts grew, and that those volatiles had escaped when the matrix formed. In this case, volatile content may have been more important than cooling rate in determining crystal size.

56. They are septarian nodules. They form during diagenesis of usually argillaceous (muddy) sediments with significant Ca or (in this case) Fe carbonate content. Water migrating through the compacting sediment pile forms carbonate-enriched concretions, usually discoid in shape, which subsequently shrink and crack as they harden. The cracks are then filled with crystalline material, usually calcite (as in this case).

The two lower examples in this group are mirror-image halves of the same nodule, broken open.

57. Not much. The picture is deliberately included to show you that many outcrops permit only limited and very general inferences to be drawn. The absence of obvious bedding and the resistant nature of the rocks (they form a hill) suggests that they might be either igneous or metamorphic. The somewhat blocky aspect suggests that the rocks might be finer- rather than coarser-grained, but that is by no means certain at this distance. The absence of outcrop to the left could be due to faulting, but that is just one of a number of possibilities.

58. (a) The grooves result from solution by rain water and ground water during the centuries of exposure to the weather.
(b) The crystal shows re-entrant angles produced by twinning. It shows up so well because the light is reflected off a cleavage.
(c) The rock is alabaster, composed of gypsum ($CaSO_4.2H_2O$), which has a perfect cleavage and twins readily. It is the first mineral to be precipitated in quantity from evaporating sea water, and is a major constituent of evaporite deposits. It also forms diagenetically in some clays.

59. (a) The base is made of a finer-grained and paler-coloured rock than the column.
(b) The column is made of a granular or crystalline rock of uniformly coarse grain size, without banding or layering (the horizontal lines are joins between blocks). The irregular dark inclusion is coarse-grained enough for white grains or crystals to be visible in it.

The rock could be a gritstone with scattered clasts of mudstone, but the absence of layering and the relatively coarse grain size of the inclusion makes this unlikely. The inclusion is more likely to be a (partly metamorphosed) xenolith in an intermediate or acid (i.e. pale-coloured) plutonic igneous rock.
(Granite column, limestone base.)

60. The stone is sandstone, the well-developed cross-bedding picked out by weathering since the building was erected. Inverted bedding is obvious in at least two blocks: the second in from the left in the second row down from the 'overhang', and the last on the right in the row below that. No doubt you can find others.